DATE DUE

Demco, Inc. 38-293

ANCIENT GLASS

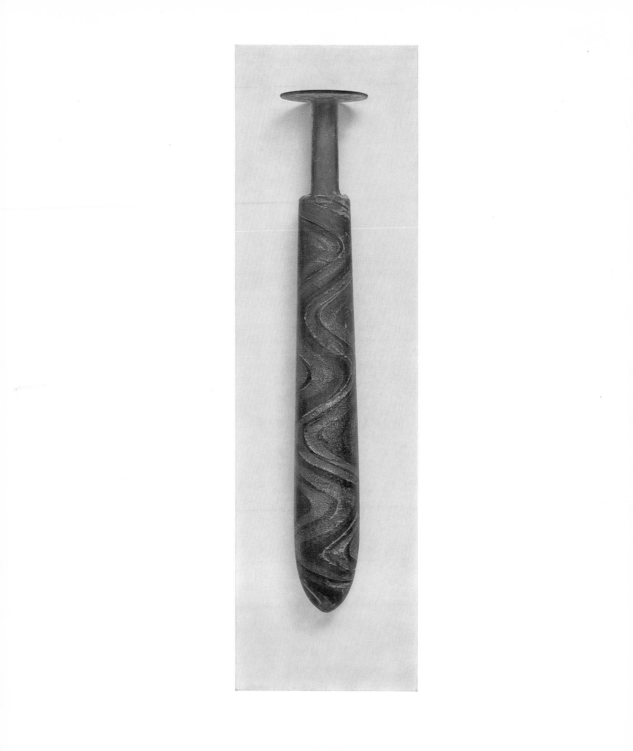

No. 16

ANCIENT

✻

GLASS

✻

in the

✻

MUSEUM

✻

OF

✻

FINE ARTS

✻

BOSTON

✻

by

✻

AXEL

✻

VON

✻

SALDERN

Copyright © 1968

by

Museum of Fine Arts

Boston

Printed by

The Meriden Gravure Co.

Meriden

Connecticut

Color plates by

Ph. von Zabern

Mainz

Germany

Designed by

Carl F. Zahn

Library of Congress Catalogue

Card No. 67-31751

"Pausing on the sandy shores of the River Belus in Syria, a group of merchants built a fire protected by slabs of saltpeter to cook their meal. The intense heat caused the saltpeter, together with the sand, to fuse in such a way that a clear substance oozed out which, after cooling, became glass." Thus the story is related by the Roman historian, Pliny. Unlikely as this tale of the discovery of glassmaking seems to us today, it does contain elements which are plausible. First, glassmaking did play a dominant role in the River Belus region, especially after the invention of the blowpipe, and Pliny, knowing this, gave his story an appropriate setting right in the center of the glass industry of the ancient world. Second, glass can indeed be a mixture of sand (silica) and saltpeter (alcali) which, when exposed to great heat, fuse together. The implausible aspect of the story lies in the fact that enormously high temperatures (about 1000 to 1100 degrees centigrade) are required to melt and fuse the raw materials, and the Syrian traders' fire could hardly have provided the necessary intensity of heat. Nonetheless, the tale provides us with a logical starting point for the discussion of the early history of glassmaking.

TECHNIQUE

The early manufacture of glass was undoubtedly concentrated, in Egypt as well as in Mesopotamia, in small workshops, where the manufacturing process was carried out in various stages. The raw materials (sand, soda, lime, and coloring agents such as cobalt for blue) were put into crucibles, and heated in small, wood-fired furnaces. After a first heating, the semi-molten material was crushed to "frit" and then melted again, a process that could be repeated until the glass was in a condition to make the manufacture of vessels possible. This was the basis of glassmaking. The numerous ways of making glass vessels and decorating them cannot all be described here, but it may suffice to mention the major ones.

Core Vessels

The earliest vessels in Egypt and Mesopotamia were made by the core process. Glass was taken from a crucible where it had been melted down and was then gathered around a solid clay core roughly the shape of the desired object. Threads of contrasting color were pulled from other crucibles, wrapped around the vessel, pressed into the hot soft surface, and combed up and down with a pointed instrument to create wave and chevron patterns. This had to be done with great speed, although it was possible when necessary to reheat the glass to a certain degree in order to recover its pliability. After cooling, the object was ground and polished to remove the excess glass of the thread pattern and to give the surface a brilliant sheen. Finally the clay core was scraped out to leave the hollow vessel (Nos. 1–5).

Molded Vessels

Another method of glass production used before the first century B.C. was the mold technique. Small decorative plaques of Mycenaean origin were formed in molds, as were Near Eastern Astarte figurines, and Assyrian vessels. For the latter, two processes were used. In the lost-wax process (copied from the manufacture of metal vessels), the object was first modeled in wax, then covered with a plaster mold; the wax was then melted and replaced by ground glass; subsequently the mold was placed in a furnace. Alternatively, ground glass was sandwiched between a positive and a negative mold; these were then bound together and placed in a furnace where heat caused slow melting and fusion of the glass (Nos. 7–10).

Blowpipe

With the introduction of the blowpipe in Syria in the second half of the first century B.C., manufacturing methods were completely changed, and mass production became possible. Simple vessels could be blown at the rate of 100 an hour. The hot glass was gathered at the end of a hollow tube through which air was blown. The bubble of glass thus formed was transferred to a solid rod; it was then reheated, cut open where the blowpipe had been attached, and manipulated with pinchers and flat pieces of wood. It was rolled back and forth on a flat hard surface such as marble until the desired shape was obtained. Various other elements such as handles, stems, and feet were then attached to the main body. Hot threads could be applied for decoration, and the glass surface could be pulled, punched, and dragged with pointed tools for additional effects (Nos. 44ff.). During the whole production process, the glass had to be periodically reheated to keep it soft enough for manipulation. After annealing (slow cooling), the finished product could be painted and gilded, either with a waterbase paint or with an enamel paint which, after firing, formed an inseparable bond with the glass (No. 70).

Cut Designs

In order to cut designs into the surface of the glass after cooling, the object could be scratched with a hard instrument such as a diamond, or it could be pressed against a rotating copper wheel fed with an abrasive such as emery powder (No. 27). Tours de force of decoration such as the diatreta vessels were worked in the following way: a thick vessel was undercut — possibly with tools similar to our dentist drills — so that an inner bowl remained surrounded by an outer net; the two were held together by the tiny ridges which the carver left standing. These were so difficult

No. 63   No. 50   No. 36

to make that only a very few, particularly patient master craftsmen could have produced them. Some of the vessels were first enveloped in one or two layers of contrasting color which, when cut down to a net or an inscriptive frieze, formed a delicate polychrome skin around the colorless inner bowl.

Cameo Glass

Cameo glass was made in imitation of real cameo work. A vessel of one color was covered with one or more layers of contrasting color – generally blue overlaid by white. The artisan would then cut away portions of the white glass until the desired design was achieved (Nos. 24–25).

Mold-Blown Glass

An inexpensive and convenient way to inscribe decorative patterns on simple vessels was to cut the desired motif on the inside of a ceramic or wooden mold. A bubble of glass blown into the mold would then receive the impression of the pattern (Nos. 29–43). The wooden mold would not burn because it had been dampened beforehand, creating a steam film which protected it from the red-hot glass.

Mosaic and Millefiori Glass

This method is simultaneously a manufacturing and a decorative process. Mosaic and millefiori glass are the most colorful category in the medium. Both varieties are basically the same. In millefiori glass, threads of glass of contrasting color are arranged in such a way that a bundle of them shows, in cross section, a floral or geometric motif. Such a bundle is heated until the various elements fuse together. It is then pulled to extend its length, reducing the diameter without destroying the motif in the cross section. The multicolored cane is then sliced, and the slices are either used for inlays or they are arranged in molds to form vessels (Nos. 13–15).

In mosaic glass, figurative and geometric motifs are put together like a jigsaw puzzle and fused to form tiles or vessels – a method first introduced in Mesopotamia in the fifteenth century B.C. In early Roman Imperial times, monochrome elements were cut into slices and manipulated into spirals which, arranged in a mold, were fused to form bowls (No. 15). The terms mosaic and millefiori can often be used interchangeably; if floral motifs are dominant, the latter term is usually preferred, as it has been employed by the Venetian glassmakers to describe vases built up of elements with floral designs.

A closely related technique is that of ribbon glass, in which bands of contrasting colored glass are laid side by side and then arranged in molds or around a core for fusion (Nos. 16–17).

HISTORY

The history of ancient glass covers a period from about 1500 B.C. to A.D. 1400; very few objects antedate the mid-second millennium B.C. Its course is continuous, i.e. there was probably not one single century during which glass manufacture stopped completely. It is a well-known fact that within these three thousand years three categories stand out among the other glass: Egyptian glass of the New Empire[1], particularly of Dynasty XVIII; Roman glass, covering almost the total area of the Roman Empire[2] and ranging from the late first century B.C. to the early fifth century A.D.; and Islamic glass of Egypt and the Near East, dating from the seventh to the fourteenth century A.D.

Archaeological investigation, especially in the last few decades, has contributed much to our knowledge of the periods and regions not covered by these three great epochs of glassmaking. We now know that in Mesopotamia, beginning about 1500 B.C., important workshops and factories existed which rose to considerable prominence in the fourteenth and in the seventh centuries B.C. Their Achaemenian and Hellenistic successors in the Near East and in Alexandria produced equally important series of glassware. From the seventh century on, Syria specialized in core-formed vessels not unlike the earlier Egyptian glass. After the collapse of the Roman Empire, relatively large establishments resumed work in northwestern Europe, as well as in Iraq and Iran where Sassanian rule apparently made a new flowering of the glass industry possible. Undoubtedly some of the Byzantine Emperors must also have promoted glass manufacture although we know nothing of it.

The invention of glassmaking was preceded by the use of glazes — chemically silica-base substances — that were applied to ceramic objects to give them a hard, shiny, and colorful surface. The earliest actual glass objects were small amulets and beads. A few of these have been dated from the period of about 2500 to 1500 B.C., but this dating is still open to doubt.

With the advent of the New Kingdom in Egypt (1580–1050) a steadily

---

1. The term "New Empire glass" is restricted to core-formed glass and inlays, notwithstanding a few mosaic vessels, and covers a region stretching from Thebes to Tell el-Amarna. Hellenistic glass is not yet fully investigated. Doubtless it was made in Alexandria, in various, still unknown centers in the Near East, and in Greece.

2. The term "Roman Empire" is used to describe glass production within the boundaries of the Empire, particularly in Syria, Egypt, Italy, Switzerland, the Rhineland, France, and England. As many types of glass are international and, therefore, their origin difficult to verify, this term is convenient though imprecise.

increasing glass production of predominantly deep blue and turquoise perfume containers, inlays, and beads supplied the court and the wealthy families with objects colorful in appearance, skillfully executed, and less expensive than the precious or semiprecious materials generally used. Perfume containers of cored glass, their forms derived from stone and ceramic prototypes, became relatively common during the latter part of Dynasty XVIII, in the late fifteenth and fourteenth centuries B.C. Lotus palm columns (No. 1), amphoriskoi, vases, and lentoid flasks occur more often than goblets and jugs which, in three exceptional cases, received cartouches of the Pharaoh Tuthmosis III. Numerous beads and inlays for furniture and masks also left the workshops; the most famous glass inlays still adorn the mask of Tutankamon. Glass, from Dynasty XIX onwards, becomes relatively rare. A few monochrome vessels seem to represent the last efforts of the Egyptian glassmakers before the turn of the millennium.

No other region during this period has produced the wealth of material that has been discovered in Egypt. A series of cored vessels, as well as a group of bowls and beakers of mosaic glass of which the earliest seem to date from after 1500 B.C., indicate, however, that Mesopotamia, too, had developed a glassmaking technique similar to the Egyptian. Which country came first, no one can yet say. Late Mycenaean and Minoan sites have also yielded large quantities of pressed ornaments and beads of blue glass, undoubtedly of local manufacture. A steatite mold from Mycenae in the Museum collection with designs for a variety of beads can be dated about 1250 B.C.

At the beginning of the first millennium, new types emerged from Mesopotamia, heralding the advent of a particularly diverse glass production in the Near East that was to last for many centuries. Assyrian sites of the late eighth and seventh centuries have disclosed a number of vessels of thick transparent glass which in all probability were made in competition with rock crystal. Many of them have been found in Nimrud. In addition, countless ivories excavated at this capital as well as in Syria were often inlaid with blue, green, and even polychrome glass, apparently dating from the ninth to the seventh century B.C. Related to these finds are some bowls and alabastra unearthed in Italy, Cyprus and the Near East which were manufactured either in Assyria or Syria. The heavily incrusted alabastron (No. 7) well represents this rare group. Thus, the Mesopotamian glass industry producing the cored perfume containers of the fifteenth century B.C. may never have been terminated. The colorful and technically superior mosaic glass discovered in Iraq and Western Iran and datable to the second half of the second and early first millennium, a few cored alabastra of the ninth or eighth centuries, and the heavy vessels of the Nimrud type indicate the various stages of a manufacturing process that served the need for luxury ware.

Beginning in the sixth century B.C. sizeable quantities of cored amphoriskoi, alabastra, and oenochoes as well as innumerable beads left workshops which were probably located along the Syrian coast. The glass was made in imitation of the New Empire ware though new shapes were adopted; its quality, initially quite remarkable, deteriorated progressively until Hellenistic times. A substantial percentage of these vessels was exported, probably by Phoenician traders to the countries bordering the Mediterranean. Even today, they are erroneously referred to as "Phoenician glass," (Nos. 2–5) and practically all the vessels in this category now preserved come from excavations outside Syria.

Glass production in the Two Stream Land (Mesopotamia) and in Syria probably never actually subsided until the fall of the Byzantine Empire over 1500 years later. Under the Achaemenid rulers, cutting shops turned out elaborately fashioned vessels patterned after silver and gold prototypes, of which, however, only a very few have been found. A steady increase in production of glass vessels and jewelry took place in Hellenistic times. Again, Egypt assumed a leading role after the founding of Alexandria in 332 B.C., a town that rapidly became renowned as a center of luxurious living. Cored glass from Syria went out of fashion during the last century before the Christian era, while the bead and pendant production (No. 6), mostly patterned after older prototypes like the eye beads, flourished under the Ptolemaic followers of Alexander the Great. Among the most popular Hellenistic glass was a bowl type that varies from a hemisphere to a more shallow shape and is made of greenish, amber, or blue glass; one or more cut grooves encircle it on the exterior or interior. It links the highly decorated carved bowls of Achaemenid and early Hellenistic periods with the pillar-molded bowls of Imperial times (Nos. 8, 11).

A technological advance and the advent of the Roman Empire at the end of the first century B.C., mark the beginning of glass production in a modern sense. The invention of the blowpipe somewhere in Syria, possibly in the area of Sidon, revolutionized this craft, making it possible to increase the output a thousandfold. The introduction of new and manifold forms and the perfecting of decorative techniques characterize this sudden outburst of glass manufacture. Its spread was swift, not only to many centers of the Near East and from there to Italy, but also following Roman colonization to the north and west, establishing itself in areas known today as Switzerland, Austria and the Rhineland, France, and England. Doubtless, more glass was made in the first century A.D. than

No. 15

No. 21

in all the 1500 previous years together. The material became attainable to all, as inexpensive and replaceable as simple pottery.

At the same time luxury vessels were patiently formed and embellished by skilled hands, catering to the refined tastes of the wealthy Romans and their prosperous subjects. A highly specialized cutting shop attached to a glass-house near Alexandria, or perhaps one of the newly established "branches" in Italy, was responsible for the fine skyphos (No. 10) in Boston. A metal vessel still served as its model.

Mosaic glass (assumed by many to be the ancient murrhine of fame) and millefiori glass (so called because it resembles "a thousand flowers") appear to have been made in Alexandria, although this has not so far been corroborated by the archaeologist. The city's reputation as the center of the luxury industry and the fact that in Egypt there existed a tradition in polychrome variegated glass, from Dynasty XVIII bowls to fourth century B.C. inlays, make it almost certain that much of this glass originates from Alexandria. In addition, shops in Syria as well as in Italy may well have produced this precious appearing material. Purely the product of a glass-maker's ingenuity, polychrome mosaic and millefiori glass has delighted the collector for the past 2000 years. These variegated and colorful vessels and inlays were used to adorn the tables, furniture, and interior walls of emperor and consul, banker and regenerate alike and today have become the focal point of any collection of ancient glass. The bowls published here (Nos. 12–15) illustrate this group extremely well. The designs become even more intricate in mosaic inlay plaques in which the technical perfection of the microscopic detail work can be appreciated only under considerable magnification (Nos. 18–19).

Glass with polychrome surface was especially popular in the first century A.D. Vessels with mottled decoration (Nos. 21–23) came in a variety of forms. Even the mold-blown jug in the Hermitage in Leningrad, signed by the famous glassmaker Ennion, received this additional adornment. A group of French glasses of the seventeenth century display an identical decoration; in much the same way Venetian millefiori glass of the Renaissance imitated Roman prototypes.

Apart from the gay, multicolored vessels and inlays cherished by the connoisseur in antiquity and in modern times alike, ancient glass attained its greatest height in the carver's workshop. The exquisitely cut plaque with the Keryneian Stag (No. 24) illustrates the cameo glass of Imperial times, the most famous example of which is the Barberini-Portland Vase in the British Museum. The few vessels and countless fragments and inlays that have survived bear witness to the technical perfection and artistic ingenuity of the Roman cameo carver. The bottle and the beaker in the Museum (Nos. 26–27) also received their decoration on the cutter's wheel. The rarity of the Venus torso (No. 28), which may have been polished after it was formed in a mold, can hardly be overemphasized as there is only one other sculpture of this type in existence. The opaque coating now covering the torso's surface is not intentional but results from the chemical decomposition of the glass while it was buried.

The elegant and costly glass vessels made up in multicolored patterns or carefully carved to meet the refined taste of the wealthy, represent only a small portion of the total production in this Empire. Very shortly after the introduction of the blowpipe, new manufacturers mushroomed throughout the countries under Roman domination. The first Syrian vessels were relatively small and blown in molds probably made of clay. The glassblowers of Sidon and Tyre on the eastern coast of the Mediterranean specialized in making cups and flasks which showed the imprint of floral and geometric motifs borrowed from the Hellenistic repertory, as well as inscriptions, various vessels, and birds (Nos. 29–36). Some of them were signed by heads of workshops such as Artas or Ennion; the latter seems to have opened a branch office in Italy early in the first century A.D.

The establishment of new factories by Syrians and the migration of Eastern craftsmen to the Roman provinces – whether traders or teachers – contributed to the dissemination of standard glass types and of technical knowledge, a fact that often makes it exceedingly difficult, if not impossible, to distinguish between a glass bowl or beaker made in Syria and one made in Italy or Gaul. Flasks in the shape of heads or grapes (Nos. 37–38) originated mostly in the East. Similarly, many of the later mold-blown glasses of the types preserved in the Boston Museum (Nos. 39–43) were made in Syria. However, simple bottles or very popular forms like the cinerary urn (No. 45) were found in great numbers in Syria, Italy, Switzerland, France, and Germany.

In the first century A.D. glass became a common commodity. The vessels illustrated here (Nos. 46–60) stand for an infinite variety of shapes and sizes which were mass-produced in the undoubtedly efficient and well-organized factories. Supplying the needs of a population with a rather high standard of living, and exporting to areas not under Roman domination, they functioned in a fashion similar to those of medieval and Renaissance Europe. Furnace construction, tools, and probably the quantity of glassware produced, did not change markedly between the first century and the industrial revolution in the nineteenth century. The "run of the mill" production of glass included: perfume bottles that were often used to ship the precious liquid to faraway places (No. 47); drinking cups and beakers (Nos. 46, 48, 50, 51); large and small storage vessels

(Nos. 45–53) ; innumerable bottles for storing oils and other liquids ; bowls and plates used probably for serving as well as for storage ; and lastly, window glass and pharmaceutical ware. Often they were enhanced to relieve the monotony of undecorated surfaces. Thus, lines were cut into the glass (Nos. 53–54), or the vessels were indented by their makers while still hot (Nos. 50–52), or threads of pliable glass were wound round them (Nos. 57–59). Molded masks were attached to give a vessel more interesting features (No. 55), or disks of contrasting color were carefully incorporated in the still soft surface (No. 61).

The fall of the Roman Empire in the late fourth and fifth centuries, affected glass production probably more severely in Europe than in the Near East. Western factories continued on a scale much reduced and their products were consequently limited to a few basic types often of poor quality glass. In a few instances, however, remarkably well-executed and attractive vessels of Frankish origin have been excavated in western and northern Europe. In countries along the eastern Mediterranean the downfall of the Empire may not have noticeably impeded the production of glass. Regions within the realm of the Byzantine and Sassanian power structures continued to prosper, affording glass factories the opportunity to produce vessels stylistically derived from Roman ware and forming a link to the impressive upsurge under Islamic domination. It may be that a heavily cut bottle in the Museum collection (No. 63) originates from Iraq, representing the luxury glass manufacture of the period.

Coincidental with the ascent of powerful political structures were the great periods in the history of ancient glass. Under the Islamic Caliphates, for example, the final, and in some respects most glorious, stage of ancient glass took place. Apart from the innumerable free-blown vessels, mold-blown (Nos. 66–68) and cut glass left the workshops in Iraq and Iran, in Syria and Egypt ; others had thread decoration embedded in the surface (No. 69), similar to the Roman glass of many centuries earlier. The greatest artistry, however, is evident in the lavishly embellished en-ameled and gilded beakers, bottles, and mosque lamps which seem to have been decorated predominantly in Damascus and Aleppo. The fine design on the beaker illustrated here (No. 70) is now largely obscured by the weathering of the glass after long burial.

The conquest of the Near East by the Mongols about A.D. 1400 termi-nated glass manufacture that had lasted for 3500 years. The mantle now was inherited by Venice and a true Renaissance in glass was under way in the Western World.

The glass collection in the Museum of Fine Arts amounts to about 750 pieces. The majority comes from the Near East, probably almost exclusively from Syrian factories operating during the Roman Empire. Most of them are datable to the first to fourth centuries A.D. A group of about three dozen vessels are core-formed and were made in Syria during the second half of the first millennium B.C. Products of glass-houses in Egypt during the New Empire, in Assyria, in Hellenistic centers, in regions under Frankish and Sassanian rule, and in the large Islamic cities are sparsely represented in Boston.

1. PALM COLUMN, Egypt, New Kingdom, late
Dynasty XVIII, *ca.* 1400–1300 B.C. Blue glass
made in the core process and decorated with
white and yellow threads. H.: 3¾ in. (0.095m.).
M. Elizabeth Carter Collection. 18.270.

2. ALABASTRON, Eastern Mediterranean, *ca.* 4th–3rd
century B.C. Deep blue with white and yellow threads.
Bought in Athens, together with a very similar alabastron,
by E. P. Warren and said to have been found in Cyrene.
H.: 5¾ in. (0.145m.). *H. L. Pierce Fund. 01.8219.*

3. ALABASTRON, Eastern Mediterranean, *ca.* 6th–4th
century B.C. Blue with polychrome feather pattern.
H. : 5⁷⁄₁₆ in. (0.138m.). *Gift of the Archaeological
Institute of America. 84.14.*

4. ALABASTRON, Eastern Mediterranean, *ca.* 4th–2nd
century B.C. Blue with yellow and turquoise threads.
Said to have been found at Assos. H. : 4⅜ in. (0.11m.).
Gift of the Archaeological Institute of America. 84.15.

5. OENOCHOE, Eastern Mediterranean, *ca*. 6th–4th century B.C. White with blue thread decoration, a combination less frequent than the white-and-purple scheme in late cored glass. Purchased in Greece by E. P. Warren. H.: 4⅜ in. (0.11m.). *H. L. Pierce Fund. 99.445.*

6. HEAD BEAD, Egypt or Eastern Mediterranean,
Ptolemaic. Turquoise with inlays and applications in
yellow and blue. Purchased in Athens by E. P. Warren;
from Thebes. H.: 2 in. (0.051m.). *H. L. Pierce Fund.*
01.8234.

7. ALABASTRON, Assyria or Syria, 7th–6th
century B.C. Thick greenish glass with golden
iridescence, formed (in the lost wax process?)
and ground. Said to be from Cyprus. H.: 5¹³⁄₁₆ in.
(0.148m.). *Gift of Mrs. S. W. Whitman. 87.50.*

8. BOWL, Near East or Italy, late Hellenistic, probably 1st century B.C. Light blue, cut grooves on the interior; formed (in the lost wax process?) and ground. H.: 2½ in. (0.063m.); D.: 4¾ in. (0.12m.). *Gift of Martin Brimmer. 86.52.*

9. PYXIS, probably Crete, 3rd–1st century B.C. Thick greenish glass made in a mold
(lost wax process ?). Purchased in Crete. H. : 1⅜ in. (0.035m.) ; D. : 2¾ in. (0.069m.).
Gift of H. P. Kidder. 81.345.

10. SKYPHOS, Near East (Alexandria ?) or Italy, late Hellenistic or early Roman Imperial. Clear with gray tint, formed in a mold (probably lost wax process), ground and polished. H. : 3¼ in. (0.083m.). *Bequest of Charles B. Hoyt. 50.2285.*

11. BOWL, so-called "pillar molded bowl," Near East or Italy, late 1st century B.C.–
1st century A.D. Blue, concentric cut rings on interior center, formed in a mold.
D.: 5 in. (0.0127m.). *M. Elizabeth Carter Collection. 18.254.*

12. MOSAIC BOWL, Roman Empire, probably Alexandria or Italy, late 1st century
B.C.–1st century A.D. "Pillar-molded" type ; blue and white. D. : 4¼ in. (0.108m.).
H. L. Pierce Fund. 99.442.

13. MILLEFIORI BOWL, Roman Empire, probably Alexandria or Italy, late 1st
century B.C.–1st century A.D. Amber stars with blue and white centers, and blue and
white spirals, as well as elements of clear glass and one piece in purple and clear with
gold leaf. D. : 6¹¹⁄₁₆ in. (0.17m.). *H. L. Pierce Fund. 99.440.*

14. MILLEFIORI BOWL, Roman Empire, probably Alexandria or Italy, late 1st century B.C.–1st century A.D. Rosettes in red, white, and yellow within purple glass. Purchased in Rome by E. P. Warren. D. : 4⁹⁄₁₆ in. (0.116m.). *H. L. Pierce Fund. 99.439.*

15. MOSAIC AND MILLEFIORI BOWL, Roman Empire, probably Alexandria or
Italy, late 1st century B.C.–1st century A.D. Purple bands divide surface into sections
which contain blue stars as well as spirals in purple and white, and amber and white ;
they are imbedded in a turquoise matrix. H. : 3 in. (0.075m.) ; D. : 5⅜ in. (0.137m.).
Gift of Edward P. Warren. 93.144.

16. RIBBON GLASS ALABASTRON, Roman Empire,
probably Alexandria or Italy, late 1st century B.C.–1st
century A.D. Ribbons of green, blue, and gold glass.
Purchased, together with the very similar alabastron 98.939,
by E. P. Warren. Said to be from Palestrina. H.: 7¹/₁₆ in.
(0.179m.). *H. L. Pierce Fund. 98.938.*

17. RIBBON GLASS PYXIS, Roman Empire, probably Alexandria or Italy, late
1st century B.C.—early 1st century A.D. Ribbons of blue, purple, green, and gold
glass. Engraved grooves and rings on cover, around walls, and at base of vessel.
H. (with cover) : 2⅝ in. (0.067m.). *H. L. Pierce Fund. 99.454.*

18. MOSAIC INLAY, Roman Empire, Eastern Mediterranean or Italy, 1st century
B.C.–1st century A.D. Floral motif in yellow, purple, white and red, inlaid in green.
Purchased in Rome by E. P. Warren. 1⅞ in. x 1 in. (0.048m. x 0.027m.). *H. L. Pierce
Fund. 01.8228.*

19. MOSAIC INLAY, probably Roman Empire, about 1st century
B.C.–1st century A.D. Blue glass with white backing, inlaid
in cloisonné with a green acanthus. D.: ⅝ in. (0.017 m.).
H. L. Pierce Fund. 01.8235.

20. BOTTLE, Roman Empire, Near East or Italy, 1st century A.D. Deep amber
with threads of white glass arranged in waves. H. : 6¼ in. (0.158m.).
M. Elizabeth Carter Collection. 28.223.

21. CRATER, Roman Empire, Near East or Italy, 1st century A.D. Light blue with mottled dot pattern in green, red, and white. Purchased by E. P. Warren in Athens. H. : 4⅜ in. (0.111m.) ; D. : 5¾ in. (0.146m.). *H. L. Pierce Fund. 99.456.*

22. VASE, Roman Empire, Near East or Italy, 1st century A.D. Purple with mottled decoration in white. H.: 5¾ in. (0.145m.); D.: 6 in. (0.153m.). *H. L. Pierce Fund. 99.444.*

23. AMPHORA, Roman Empire, Near East (or Italy ?), 1st century A.D.
Blue, with mottled decoration in white, blue, and yellow. Purchased in
Athens by E. P. Warren. H.: 5¼ in. (0.133m.). *H. L. Pierce Fund.*
01.8225.

24. CAMEO GLASS PLAQUE, Roman Empire, probably Italy, about
late 1st–early 2nd century A.D. White on blue cut cameo glass with
"Heracles Slaying the Keryneian Stag." 1⅞ in. x ¾ in. (0.047m. x 0.02m.).
Francis Bartlett Fund. 13.212.

25. CAMEO GLASS FRAGMENT, Roman Empire, probably Italy, about
2nd century A.D. White on blue cut cameo glass; visible are the upper
half of a woman (maenad ?) with a wine cup, the arm of another person,
and a tree in the background. Purchased in Rome by E. P. Warren.
1½ in. x 1½ in. (0.038m. x 0.0375m.). *H. L. Pierce Fund. 01.8236.*

26. BOTTLE, Roman Empire, Near East or Italy, 1st century A.D.
Clear blown glass with cut grooves at upper and lower body.
H.: 2¹³⁄₁₆ in. (0.072m.). *Collection of Mrs. Philip Hofer, 21*.46.

27. BEAKER, Roman Empire, Near East (or Italy ?), 2nd half 1st century A.D. Clear blown glass with cut facet pattern bordered by ridges. H. : 3⅝ in. (0.092m.). *Bequest of Charles B. Hoyt. 50.2284.*

28. VENUS TORSO, Roman Empire, Near East
(Alexandria ?) or Italy, 1st–2nd century A.D. Greenish
solid glass molded in imitation of the Cnidian Aphrodite
type. H.: 3⁷⁄₁₆ in. (0.087m.). *H. L. Pierce Fund. 99.452.*

29. CUP, Roman Empire, Syria, late 1st century B.C.—1st century
A.D. Blue, with mold-blown decoration of leaves and circlets.
H.: 1⁷⁄₁₆ in. (0.036m.) ; D.: 2⅝ in. (0.066m.). *Bequest of Charles
B. Hoyt. 50.2277.*

30. BEAKER, Roman Empire, Syria, late 1st century B.C.–early 1st century
A.D. Pale olive with mold-blown pattern, including the inscription : МИНСѲН О
ΑΓΟΡΑⱫWN (let the buyer be remembered) and a zig-zag frieze. Purchased
by E. P. Warren in London and said to be from Asia Minor. H. : 2¹⁵⁄₁₆ in.
(0.075m.) ; D. : 2⅞ in. (0.073m.). *H. L. Pierce Fund. 99.446*.

31. JUG, Roman Empire, Syria, late 1st century B.C.—early 1st
century A.D. Greenish (?, now covered with heavy iridescence)
with blue handle ; mold-blown design of chalices, jug, amphora,
rectangular object and circlets. Found near Tyre. H. : 4 in.
(0.102m.). *M. Elizabeth Carter Collection. 31.130.*

32. FLASK, Roman Empire, Syria, late 1st century B.C.–
early 1st century A.D. Blue with white handles, with mold-
blown pattern, including encircled rosettes. H. : 3¼ in.
(0.082m.). *M. Elizabeth Carter Collection. 31.132.*

33. BOTTLE, Roman Empire, Syria, late 1st century B.C.–
1st century A.D. Pale purple, with mold-blown pattern of
tendril frieze and fluting. H.: 2⅜ in. (0.06m.).
M. Elizabeth Carter Collection. 15.858.

34. JUG, Roman Empire, Syria, 1st century A.D. Pale olive-green, with mold-blown design of wreath within a pattern of "dashes." H.: 3⅝ in. (0.092m.). *M. Elizabeth Carter Collection. 28.226.*

35. BOTTLE, Roman Empire, Syria, late 1st century B.C.–1st century
A.D. Milk glass with mold-blown design of tendrils, blossoms, and
birds. H.: 3⅞ in. (0.098m.). *Bequest of Charles B. Hoyt. 50.2280.*

36. BEAKER, Roman Empire, Near East (Syria?), 1st century A.D. Clear glass with blue-green tint, covered with silver iridescence. Mold-blown design of a continuous tendril with heart-shaped leaves. H.: 3¹⁵⁄₁₆ in. (0.101 m.). *Purchased. 01.7448.*

37. HEAD FLASK, Roman Empire, Near East or Southern
Europe, about 2nd century A.D. Clear, mold-blown in form
of a head with two faces. H.: 3⅛ in. (0.08m.). *Gift of
Frederick L. Jack. 35.1431.*

38. GRAPE FLASK, Roman Empire, probably Near East, 2nd century A.D.
Olive-amber, mold-blown in form of a stylized grape. H. : 4⅝ in. (0.118m.).
Purchased. 99.78.

39. JUG, Roman Empire, probably Syria, 4th–5th century A.D. Amber, with mold-blown decoration on a hexagonal body : diamonds alternating with vertical motifs resembling the "tree of life." H. : 5³⁄₁₆ in. (0.132m.). *M. Elizabeth Carter Collection. 15.857.*

40. BOTTLE, Roman Empire, probably Near East, 3rd–4th century A.D. Clear with green tint, mold-blown pattern of a central rosette framed by irregular fretwork. H.: 6¾ in. (0.172m.). *M. Elizabeth Carter Collection. 22.626.*

41. BOWL, Roman Empire, probably Near East, about 4th century A.D. Light
olive-green, mold-blown pattern of four festoons like arches and verticals framing
oval motifs. H.: 4 in. (0.102m.) ; D.: 4¹⁵⁄₁₆ in. (0.125m.). *Bequest of Charles B. Hoyt.*
50.2272.

42. BOWL OR LAMP, Roman Empire, probably Near East, about 4th century
A.D. Greenish, mold-blown design of diamonds with central bosses, bordered
on top by a flute frieze. H. : 3⁹⁄₁₆ in. (0.091m.) ; D. : 3³⁄₁₆ in. (0.081m.). *Bequest
of Charles B. Hoyt. 50.2271.*

43. BOTTLE, Roman Empire, probably Near East, about 2nd
century A.D. Blue-greenish, with heavy iridescence ; blown
in hexagonal mold. H. : 3¹⁵⁄₁₆ in. (0.1m.). *M. Elizabeth Carter
Collection. 28.227.*

44. BOTTLE, Roman Empire, probably Near East, about 3rd century A.D. Heavy blue glass. H. : 6 in. (0.153m.). *Gift of Frederick L. Jack. 35.1434.*

45. CINERARY URN, Roman Empire, late 1st century A.D. Pale green; the cover originally did not belong to the urn. H. (with cover): 14½ in. (0.367m.); H. (without cover): 10½ in. (0.276m.). *John M. Rodocanachi Fund. 48.1246.*

46. GOBLET, Roman Empire, Syria or Egypt, probably about 4th–5th century A.D.
Thin clear glass. H.: 3¹⁄₁₆ in. (0.078m.) ; D.: 3⅜ in. (0.085m.). *M. Elizabeth Carter Collection. 28.224.*

47. "TEARBOTTLE," Roman Empire, Near East, about 2nd–3rd century A.D. Pale blue-green. H.: 6¾ in. (0.172m.). *Gift of the Misses Amy and Clara Curtis. 21.1363.*

48. CUP, Roman Empire, Near East, 1st century A.D. Pale blue-green, with pair of faintly engraved lines. H.: 2¹⁵⁄₁₆ in. (0.075m.). *Purchased. 72.423.*

49. BOTTLE, Roman Empire, Near East, about 4th–5th century A.D.
Clear with yellow tint, two threads applied to neck. H.: 6½ in. (0.165m.).
Gift of the Misses Amy and Clara Curtis. 21.1365.

50. VESSEL, Roman Empire, Eastern Mediterranean, 2nd–3rd century A.D. Pale green, with nine indentations. Said to have been found in Syria. H.: 6½ in. (0.165m.). *Gift of Mrs. W. Scott Fitz. 07.114.*

51. BEAKER, Roman Empire, Eastern Mediterranean, 2nd–3rd century
A.D. Thin clear glass, tooled to form four sides with indentations.
H.: 4⅛ in. (0.105m.). *Purchased. 72.429.*

52. BOTTLE WITH COVER, Roman Empire, Eastern Mediterranean, 2nd–3rd century
A.D. Greenish, tooled to form four deep indentations. H. (with cover) : 5⅝ in.
(0.143m.). *Gift of Dr. William N. Bullard. 90.71.*

53. BOTTLE, Roman Empire, probably Eastern Mediterranean, 2nd–early 3rd century A.D. Pale olive-green, with seven faintly engraved lines. Said to be from Crete. H.: 9⁷⁄₁₆ in. (0.24m.). *Gift of Martin Brimmer. 86.35.*

54. BEAKER, Roman Empire, Eastern Mediterranean, late 1st–2nd century A.D.
Clear, with four engraved lines. Said to be from Crete. H. : 3⁹⁄₁₆ in. (0.091m.).
Gift of Martin Brimmer. 86.48.

55. JUG, Roman Empire, probably Near East, 3rd century A.D. Deep blue, with brilliant iridescence ; the blown jug has an applied and molded grotesque mask on its obverse side. H. : 6³⁄₁₆ in. (0.157m.) ; Depth of mask : ¾ in. (0.02m.). *M. Elizabeth Carter Collection. 31.411.*

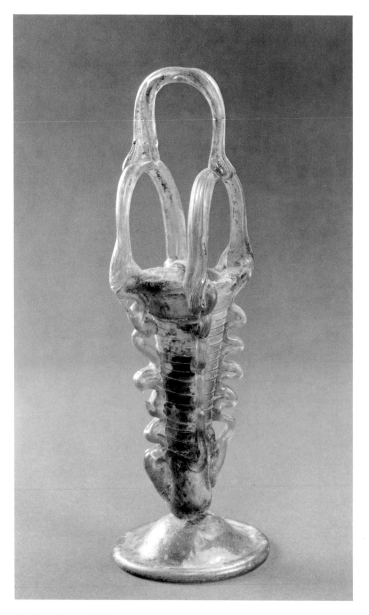

56. BALSAMARIUM, Roman Empire, Near East, late 3rd–early 5th century
A.D. Greenish single-tube vessel with applied thread decoration and basket
handle. H. : 8¾ in. (0.222m.). *Purchased. 01.7450.*

57. VASE, Roman Empire, probably Syria, about 3rd century A.D. Clear glass
with heavy iridescence, applied threads in turquoise glass. H. : 2³⁄₁₆ in. (0.055m.).
M. Elizabeth Carter Collection. 18.264.

58. JUG, Roman Empire, probably Syria, about 3rd century A.D. Pale blue-green
with applied threads in dark blue-green glass. Said to be from vicinity of Tyre.
H.: 5⅛ in. (0.13m.). *Everett Fund. 93.13.*

59. JUG, Roman Empire, probably Syria, about 3rd century A.D.
Clear with heavy iridescence, applied decoration in turquoise glass.
H. : 4⅞ in. (0.123m.). *M. Elizabeth Carter Collection. 30.403.*

60. DOLPHIN ARYBALLOS, Roman Empire, Eastern Mediterranean, late 1st–2nd century A.D. Pale green, with dolphin-like handles to which a bronze handle is attached. H. : 2⅞ in. (0.073m.). *H. L. Pierce Fund*. *01.8227*.

61. BEAKER (OR LAMP ?), Roman Empire, Near East, late 4th–early 5th century A.D. Clear (?), with heavy iridescence. Applied dots of dark blue glass arranged in two groups of six alternating with single dots. H. : 5⅞ in. (0.15m.). *M. Elizabeth Carter Collection. 30.394.*

62. VASE, Near East, possibly early Islamic (7th–8th century A.D. ?). Brown with purple iridescence ; decorated with red and white threads tooled to form a feather and loop pattern. Said to have come from Phoenicia. H. : 2³⁄₁₆ in. (0.055m.). *Gift of Mrs. S. D. Warren. 94.203.*

63. BOTTLE, possibly Iraq, 6th–8th century A.D. Thick clear glass with cut decoration of three rows of countersunk disks, nine in each row and placed against hexagons. H. : 5⅝ in. (0.143m.). *Bequest of Charles B. Hoyt. 50.1741.*

64. HORSE BALSAMARIUM, Near East, about 6th–8th century A.D. Pale olive-green; the vial is supported by a horse (some threads restored). H.: 5 in. (0.128m.). *M. Elizabeth Carter Collection. 29.967.*

65. JUG, Near East, Islamic, about 7th–9th century A.D. Green, mold-blown decoration of stylized Cufic inscription "El Malek" (for the King). Said to have been found near Damascus. H.: 3^{15}/$_{16}$ in. (0.1m.). *M. Elizabeth Carter Collection. 31.133.*

66. BOTTLE, Near East, Islamic, about 10th–12th century A.D. Greenish glass, mold-blown with ornamental decoration. H. : 3¹³⁄₁₆ in. (0.093m.). *M. Elizabeth Carter Collection. 18.265.*

67. BOTTLE, Near East, Islamic, about 10th–12th century
A.D. Greenish, mold-blown with ornamental decoration.
H.: 3⅛ in. (0.08m.). *M. Elizabeth Carter Collection. 30.218.*

68. BOTTLE, Near East, Islamic, about 10th–12th century A.D. Clear,
mold-blown with ornamental decoration. H.: 4⅞ in. (0.124m.).
M. Elizabeth Carter Collection. 30.225.

69. BOTTLE, Near East, Islamic, probably 8th–
10th century A.D. Olive, with embedded scales
of white glass. H.: 3¾ in. (0.095m.). *M. Elizabeth
Carter Collection. 18.273.*

70. BEAKER, Islamic, Syria, probably Damascus, late 13th–early 14th century A.D. Clear, with heavy iridescent scum. Enameled and gilded (much destroyed) with a Cufic inscription band and a fish pattern. H.: 5½ in. (0.14m.). *M. Elizabeth Carter Collection. 30.393.*

FOR FURTHER READING

Dan Barag	"Mesopotamian Glass Vessels of the Second Millennium B.C.," *Journal of Glass Studies*, IV (1962), pp. 9–27.
H. C. Beck	"Glass Before 1500 B.C.," *Ancient Egypt and the East*, Part I (1934), pp. 7–21.
Ludwig Berger	*Römische Gläser aus Vindonissa* (Basel, 1960).
Corning Museum of Glass	*Glass from the Ancient World, the R.W. Smith Collection* (Corning, 1957) (with good bibliography).
Gladys R. Davidson	*Corinth, XII. The Minor Objects* (Princeton, 1952).
G. A. Eisen	*Glass* (New York, 1927).
Fritz Fremersdorf	*Figürlich geschliffene Gläser . . .* (Berlin, 1951).
Fritz Fremersdorf	*Das naturfarbene sogenannte blaugrüne Glas in Köln* (Cologne, 1958).
Fritz Fremersdorf	*Römisches Buntglas aus Köln* (Cologne, 1958).
Fritz Fremersdorf	*Geformtes Glas in Köln* (Cologne, 1961).
Poul Fossing	*Glass Vessels Before Glass-Blowing* (Copenhagen, 1940).
Wilhelm Froehner	*Collection Julien Gréau. Verrerie . . . appartenant à M. John Pierpont Morgan* (Paris, 1903).
Waldemar Haberey	"Spätantike Gläser aus Gräbern von Mayen," *Bonner Jahrbücher*, 147 (1942).
D. B. Harden	*Roman Glass from Karanis* (Ann Arbor, 1936).
D. B. Honey	*Glass. A Handbook . . .* (Vict. and Albert Mus.) (London, 1946).
Clasina Isings	*Roman Glass from Dated Finds* (Groningen, 1957).
Anton Kisa	*Das Glas im Altertume* (Leipzig, 1908).
C. J. Lamm	*Mittelalterliche Gläser und Steinschnittarbeiten aus dem Nahen Osten* (Berlin, 1929/30).
Liège	*Trois millénaires d'art verrier . . .* (Liège, 1958).
Siegfried Loeschcke	*Beschreibung römischer Altertümer gesammelt von C. A. Niessen* (Cologne, 1911).
Morin-Jean	*La verrerie en Gaule sous l'Empire Romain* (Paris, 1913).
Frederic Neuburg	*Ancient Glass* (London, 1962).
C. J. Phillips	*Glass. The Miracle Maker* (New York - London, 1948) (technological treatise).
A. von Saldern	"Glass Finds at Gordion," *Journal of Glass Studies*, I (1959), pp. 23–54.
Giorgio Sangiorgi	*Collezione di vetri antichi* (Milan-Rome, 1914).
Christoph Simonett	*Tessiner Gräberfelder* (Basel, 1941).
Mary Louella Trowbridge	*Philological Studies in Ancient Glass* (Univ. of Illinois, 1930).

G. Davidson Weinberg   "Hellenistic Glass Vessels from the Athenian Agora," *Hesperia*, XXX (1961), pp. 380–392.

Robert Zahn   *Sammlung Baurat Schiller*, sales cat. Lepke (Berlin, 1929).

Many of the more recent publications have ample bibliographies. Particularly the numerous studies of F. Fremersdorf, W. Haberey, T. E. Haevernick, D. B. Harden and G. D. Weinberg contain a wealth of important material. Relatively complete bibliographies published since 1956 are included in the yearly *Journal of Glass Studies*, edited by The Corning Museum of Glass.

NOTES

1. 18.270. See Poul Fossing, *Glass Vessels Before Glass-Blowing* for the most complete account on cored glass of Egypt and the Eastern Mediterranean; for this type see esp. p. 22 and Fig. 14. Published: A. v. Saldern, *MFA Bulletin*, 64, 1966, p. 5f., Fig. 1.

2. 01.8219. The parallel piece in Boston is 01.8220. The standard reference work is Fossing's book, cited above; see esp. Fig. 98. See also W. Froehner, *Collection Gréau*, Pl. XII, 3. There are about 40 examples of Eastern Mediterranean cored ware in Boston. Published: A. v. Saldern, *MFA Bulletin*, 64, 1966, p. 5f., Fig. 2.

3. 84.14. See Fossing, *Glass Vessels*, pp. 58ff., 87ff. For pattern see F. Neuburg, *Glass in Antiquity*, London, 1949, Fig. 17.

4. 84.15. See F. Neuburg, *Ancient Glass*, Fig. 10. For more ornate vessels of this type see Froehner, *Collection Gréau*, Pl. II.

5. 99.445. See Fossing, *Glass Vessels*, pp. 44, 74–5; F. Neuburg, *Ancient Glass*, Fig. 9, with a white and purple oenochoe.

6. 01.8234. This pendant is representative of the great mass of glass jewelry — particularly beads of contrasting colors — that was popular in the ancient world from the New Kingdom onwards. For similar caricature heads see Froehner, *Collection Gréau*, Pl. XXVI. For glass jewelry in general see A. Kisa, *Das Glas im Altertume*, I, pp. 126ff. For the earliest glass beads see H. C. Beck, "Glass Before 1500 B.C.," pp. 9ff.

7. 87.50. This is one of a group of alabastra found in the Near East, Cyprus, and Italy which are related to glass vessels found in Nimrud as well as to glass inlays from ivories. See A. v. Saldern, "Glass Finds at Gordion," pp. 23–34. Published: A. v. Saldern, *Nimrud and its Remains*, II, 1966, p. 626; *idem*, *MFA Bulletin*, 64, 1966, p. 5f., Fig. 3.

8. 86.52. These bowls, many of which are of greenish, yellowish or amber glass, used to be called Roman until very recently. See G. D. Weinberg, "Hellenistic Glass Vessels from the Athenian Agora," pp. 380–392; A. v. Saldern, "Glass Finds at Gordion," pp. 43–44. See also O. Vessberg, "Glass," *The Swedish Cyprus Expedition*, IV, part 3, Stockholm-Lund, 1956, p. 128. —There are three bowls of this type in Boston.

9. 81.345. For a full discussion of this group see G. D. Weinberg, "Glass Manufacture in Ancient Crete," *Journal of Glass Studies*, 1, 1959, pp. 11–21; the pyxis is published under No. 10, Fig. 9.

10. 50.2285. The shape is based on silver prototypes. For similar skyphoi see G. Eisen, *Glass*, Pl. 15 (Louvre); G. Sangiorgi, *Vetri antichi*, No. 138; Anne-Marie Berryer, *La verrerie ancienne aux Musées Royaux d'Art et d'Histoire*, Bruxelles, 1957, Fig. 3 (from Kertch); mounted from Siverskaia, southern Russia, now in Moscow: *Ars Orientalis*, II, 1957, Fig. 4. Published: MFA, *Illustrated Handbook*, Boston, 1964, pp. 100–101, illus.; A. v. Saldern, *MFA Bulletin*, 64, 1966, p. 7f., Fig. 4.

11. 18.254. "Pillar-molded" bowls were found all over the Roman Empire; most of them are of greenish or yellowish glass. They are derived from late Hellenistic bowls. For discussions on this type cf. D. B. Harden, "Roman Tombs at Vasa: The Glass,"

Rep. Dpt. Antiqu., Cyprus, 1940–48, 1955, pp. 49ff.; *idem,* in: C. F. C. Hawkes and R. Hull, *Camulodunum* . . ., Oxford, 1947, pp. 287–307; F. Fremersdorf, *Römisches Buntglas,* Pl. 24ff.; C. Isings, *Roman Glass from Dated Finds,* No. 3. For the derivation cf. also G. Eckholm, "De ribbade glasskålarnas ursprung," *Fornvännen,* 1958, 1–2, pp. 17–25. In Boston half a dozen vessels are of this type.

12. 99.442; purchased from E. P. Warren. For similar pieces cf. Corning, *Glass from the Ancient World,* No. 127 (with parallels found in Luxemburg and Denmark); J. Hackin, *Recherches archéologiques à Begram,* Paris, 1939, Pl. XXVI; C. Simonett, *Tessiner Gräberfelder,* Pl. 9, 4. Published: MFA, *Illustrated Handbook,* Boston, 1964, pp. 100–101, illus.; A. v. Saldern, *MFA Bulletin,* 64, 1966, p. 8f., Fig. 5.

13. 99.440; purchased from E. P. Warren. For a rich assemblage of millefiori glass cf. Froehner's monumental work, *Collection Gréau,* Vol. II.

14. 99.439. Published: G. H. Chase, *Greek and Roman Antiquities,* Boston, 1950, p. 168, Fig. 228; revised edition, 1963, pp. 236, 276, Fig. 281.

15. 93.144. Parallels for this bowl are, for example, in Corning; London, British Museum and Victoria and Albert Museum; New York, Metropolitan Museum; Copenhagen, Thorwaldsen Museum; etc. For a recent attempt to duplicate this technique cf. F. Schuler, "Ancient Glassmaking Techniques. The Molding Process," *Archaeology,* 12, No. 1, Spring 1959, p. 51.

16. 98.938; ex Tyszkiewicz Collection, No. 59. Polychrome ribbon glass was fashioned into pyxides and alabastra, more rarely into bottles (type: *Glass from the Ancient World,* No. 145). Similar alabastra are, for example, in Corning (No. 146); Berlin (*Journal of Glass Studies,* IV, 1962, p. 63); New York, Metropolitan Museum (Froehner, *Collection Gréau,* Pl. CXI); Rome, Sangiorgi Collection (*Vetri antichi,* No. 303); London, British Museum; Toledo (*Ancient and Near Eastern Glass,* n.d., ca. 1961, n. p.). Cf. F. Fremersdorf, "Alexandrinisches Buntglas aus einer Grabummauerung in Köln," *Germania,* 16, No. 4, Oct. 1932, pp. 278–86. Published: W. Froehner, *Collection d'Antiquités du Comte Michel Tyszkiewicz,* Paris, 1898, p. 30, No. 59. For a recent discussion see Andrew Oliver, Jr., "Late Hellenistic Glass in the Metropolitan Museum," *Journal of Glass Studies,* IX, 1967, pp. 20ff.; No. 4.

17. 99.454; purchased by E. P. Warren; ex H. Hoffmann Collection, No. 439. Cf. parallels in Corning (*Glass from the Ancient World,* No. 143); Berlin (*Journal of Glass Studies,* IV, 1962, p. 139); London, British Museum; from Aquileja (G. Mariacher, *L'arte del vetro,* Milan, 1954, Fig. 2). A similar, though smaller, pyxis is in Boston (98.940). Published: *Collection H. Hoffmann, Antiquités,* Hôtel Drouot, Paris, May 15ff., 1899, p. 106, No. 439; A. v. Saldern, *MFA Bulletin,* 64, 1966, p. 9f., Fig. 6.

18. 01.8228. Inlays such as this were used to adorn wooden furniture and interior walls. Cf. similar and identical plaques in Froehner, *Collection Gréau,* Pl. LXX; Rome, Sangiorgi collection; and Corning (*Glass from the Ancient World,* No. 117). Published: A. v. Saldern, *MFA Bulletin,* 64, 1966, p. 9f., Fig. 7.

19. 01.8235; purchased by E. P. Warren. Cf. a similar piece in Froehner, *Collection Gréau,* Pl. LXVI, 7.

20. 28.223. This fairly frequent type of the 1st century A.D. occurs usually in purple, blue, or amber glass. The decorative stripes are picked up and rolled in before the vessel is given its final shape. For shape cf. A. Kisa, *Das Glas im Altertume,* Formtafel, 56; for pattern cf. *Glass from the Ancient World,* No. 155. Cf. a so G. Eisen, *Glass,* Pl. 43 ; F. Fremersdorf, *Römisches Buntglas,* Pls. 7, 19.

21. 99.456. Bits of colored glass are laid on a marble slab and picked up by the hot glass bubble ; this technique was used almost exclusively in the first century A.D. For technique, dating etc. cf. F. Fremersdorf, "Römische Gläser mit buntgefleckter Ober-fläche," *Festschrift für August Oxé,* Darmstadt, 1938, pp. 116ff. ; Joseph H. C. Kern, "Zwei buntgefleckte Glaskelche des I. Jhts. n. Chr. in Leiden," *Archeologia Classica,* 8, fasc. 1, 1956, pp. 56–63. Cf. also L. Berger, *Römische Gläser aus Vindonissa,* pp. 33ff. ; C. Simonett, *Tessiner Gräberfelder,* Pl. 10. A crater with two handles and foot in F. Neuburg, *Glass in Antiquity,* London, 1949, Pl. 1.

22. 99.444 ; purchased by E. P. Warren ; ex Forman Collection, No. 199. This piece was exhibited in the National Exhibition of Works of Art in Leeds in 1868, lent by Mr. Forman. For references, see preceding entry. Published : *The Forman Collection, Catalogue of the Egyptian, Greek & Roman Antiquities,* I, London, June, 1899, No. 199.

23. 01.8225. For type cf. C. Isings, *Roman Glass from Dated Finds,* No. 15 ; *Glass from the Ancient World,* No. 158.

24. 13.212 ; purchased by E. P. Warren. Cameo glass was made particularly in the late 1st century B.C. and in the 1st and 2nd century A.D. ; workshops must have existed in the Near East (Syria and Egypt) as well as in Italy. Few vessels, but numerous frag-ments have survived. On rare occasions, up to five polychrome layers – instead of the usual two – were fused together and then cut. Cf. Erika Simon, *Die Portlandvase,* Mainz, 1957. For the myth see R. Graves, *The Greek Myths,* II, New York, 1955, pp. 110–112. Published : G. H. Chase, *Greek and Roman Antiquities,* Boston, 1950, p· 169, Fig. 230 ; revised edition, 1963, pp. 236, 277, Fig. 283 ; A. v. Saldern, *MFA Bul-letin,* 64, 1966, p. 10f., Fig. 8.

26. 21.*46.* An example of the carefully finished semi-luxury glassware of the 1st cen-tury B.C. This form was sometimes used for multicolored ribbonglass, cf. No. 16. (Ribbon glass examples : *Glass from the Ancient World,* No. 145 ; The Hague, Gemeen-temuseum, *Glass door de eeuwen,* 1959, No. 2 ; *Sammlung Baurat Schiller,* Graupe, Berlin, June, 1934, No. 190, Pl. 5 ; Archaeol. Museum, Split). For form cf. C. Isings, *Roman Glass from Dated Finds,* No. 7.

27. 50.2284. A representative of what could be called the most attractive glass drink-ing vessel in Roman times. Beakers and fragments of this type have been found at Begram in Afghanistan, Doura Europos in Syria, Karanis in Eygpt, Vindonissa in Switz-erland and other places. Cf. esp. Joachim Werner, "Zu älterkaiserzeitlichen Glas-bechern," *Germania,* 31, 1953, pp. 61ff. ; D. B. Harden, *Karanis,* pp. 137ff. ; L. Berger *Römische Gläser aus Vindonissa,* pp. 67ff. Cf. also G. Eckholm, in *Acta Arch.,* XXVII‵ 1956, pp. 47ff. For type cf. C. Isings, *Roman Glass from Dated Finds,* No. 21. A mold-blown imitation of Roman times in the Haaretz Mus., Tel Aviv. Published : A. v. Saldern, *MFA Bulletin,* 64, 1966, p. 10f., Fig. 9.

28. 99.452 ; purchased by E. P. Warren ; ex H. Hoffmann Collection, No. 492 Solid glass sculptures are very rare. Cf. a similar piece in Corning (*Glass from the Ancient World,* No. 188). Another Venus (?) of a different type is in the Damascus Museum. Published : *Collection H. Hoffmann, Antiquités,* Hôtel Drouot, Paris, May 15ff., 1899, No. 492 ; A. v. Saldern, *MFA Bulletin,* 64, 1966, p. 11f., Fig. 10.

29. 50.2277. Vessels of this type were produced in the workshop of Ennion. Cf. a cup with similar design in Corning (*Glass from the Ancient World*, No. 69).

30. 99.446. For the most complete publication of this group cf. D. B. Harden, "Romano-Syrian Glasses with Mould-blown Inscriptions," *Journal of Roman Studies*, XXV, Part II, 1935, pp. 163–186; the Boston beaker, which seems to be unique, is published here on p. 171, type E, a. Published also by E. Robinson, in Museum of Fine Arts, Boston, *Annual Report for 1899*, p. 109 and A. v. Saldern, *MFA Bulletin*, 64, 1966, p. 14, Fig. 12.

31. 31.130. Objects such as this are commonly referred to as "Sidonian." This designation may be correct in most cases as many bear the imprints of glass factory owners from Sidon. There are numerous parallels for this piece: cf. for example, *Glass from the Ancient World*, No. 79; G. Eisen, *Glass*, Pl. 51.—There are about a dozen early mold-blown vessels in Boston.

32. 31.132. Cf. a flask with similar design in Berlin (*Journal of Glass Studies*, IV, 1962, p. 63, No. 7). For a large group of mold-blown ware cf. G. Eisen, *Glass*, pp. 201ff.

33. 15.858; ex Khayat Collection. For two of the many parallels of this piece cf. *Glass from the Ancient World*, No. 75; G. Eisen, *Glass*, Pl. 54.

34. 28.226. For parallels cf. G. Eisen, *Glass*, Pl. 55; Froehner, *Collection Gréau*, Pl. CCVI. Published: A. v. Saldern, *MFA Bulletin*, 64, 1966, p. 14f., Fig. 13.

35. 50.2280. Cf. G. Eisen, *Glass*, Pl. 81. Published: G. H. Chase, *Greek and Roman Antiquities*, Boston, 1950, revised edition, 1963, pp. 236, 276, Fig. 280.

36. 01.7448; purchased from Azeez Khayat. For a group of large mold-blown vessels which succeed the early so-called Sidonian ware, cf. Jane Hayward, "Roman Mold-Blown Glass at Yale University," *Journal of Glass Studies*, IV, 1962, pp. 49–60. Published: G. H. Chase, *Greek and Roman Antiquities*, Boston, 1950, p. 167, Fig. 226; revised edition, 1963, pp. 236, 275, Fig. 279a.

37. 35.1431. Cf. a close parallel in *Glass from the Ancient World*, No. 285. Cf. also G. Eisen, *Glass*, Pl. 74ff.

38. 99.78; purchased from Azeez Khayat. Cf. *Glass from the Ancient World*, No. 258; F. Fremersdorf, *Römisches geformtes Glas*, Pls. 140ff. For the more naturalistic type of grape flasks cf. C. Isings, *Roman Glass from Dated Finds*, No. 91a.

39. 15.857; ex Khayat Collection. This is one of a group of mold-blown vessels of late Imperial date with designs, many of which have Christian or Jewish connotations. Cf. *Glass from the Ancient World*, No. 404 (now in the Metropolitan Museum, New York); G. Eisen, *Glass*, Pl. 128. For a complete "corpus" of designs cf. Eisen, *op. cit.*, pp. 465ff. For a full discussion of the group with Jewish symbols cf. Erwin R. Goodenough, *Jewish Symbols in the Graeco-Roman Period*, Bollingen series XXXVII, 1953, I, pp. 168–173; III, Figs. 388ff.

40. 22.626. For a similar bottle, with tendrils replacing the fretwork, cf. Froehner, *Collection Gréau*, Pl. CCIV.

41. 50.2272. Cf. a bowl with similar design, G. Eisen, *Glass*, Pl. 72, top.

42. 50.2271. For similar pieces with "honey-comb" pattern cf. *Glass from the Ancient World*, No. 420; F. Fremersdorf, *Römisches geformtes Glas*, Pl. 113. An identical design to the Boston piece appears in a rendering, G. Eisen, *Glass*, Fig. 95.

44. 35.1434. It is similar to a group of blue vessels – frequently molded jugs – which may have been made at one factory in the Near East; cf. *Glass from the Ancient World*, p. 141.

45. 48.1246. A very popular type, found in the Near East as well as in southern and western Europe. It was used as a storage vessel and as a cinerary urn. Cf. C. Isings, *Roman Glass from Dated Finds*, No. 63; Morin-Jean, *La verrerie en Gaule*, pp. 42ff.; F. Fremersdorf, *Das naturfarbene . . . Glas*, Pls. 98ff. Published: A. v. Saldern, *MFA Bulletin*, 64, 1966, p. 13f., Fig. 11.

46. 28.224. Goblets were made from the 1st century onwards, to become very frequent in middle, late, and post Imperial times. Cf. A. Kisa, *Das Glas im Altertume*, Formtafel, No. 329; D. B. Harden, *Karanis*, Nos. 479–481; A. v. Saldern, "Glass from Sardis," *AJA*, 66, 1962, pp. 9–10; C. Isings, *Roman Glass from Dated Finds*, No. 111.

47. 21.1363. Cf. O. Vessberg, "Roman Glass in Cyprus," *Opuscula Archaeologica*, 7, 1952, Pl. IX, 2.

48. 72.423; purchased from General di Cesnola. Cf. Vessberg, *loc. cit.* Pl. III, 11; C. Isings, *Roman Glass from Dated Finds*, No. 12.

49. 21.1365. Cf. F. Neuburg, *Ancient Glass*, Fig. 61.

These three blown vessels (Nos. 47–49) represent the common ware of Roman times; Nos. 47 and 48 in particular have been found by the thousands all over the ancient world.

50: 07.114; **51:** 72.429; purchased from General di Cesnola; **52:** 90.71. This group also represents the common "run of the mill" ware usually of Syrian provenance. Vessels with indentations begin to occur in the late 1st century A.D.; they are found in the Near East, Cyprus, Italy, Gaul and the Rhineland. For the beaker, No. 51, cf. C. Isings, *Roman Glass from Dated Finds*, No. 32; F. Fremersdorf, *Das naturfarbene . . . Glas*, Pl. 18 (cf. for this D. B. Harden's review of the book in *Germania*, 37, 1959, p. 339); Froehner, *Collection Gréau*, Pl. CCXVIII; S. Loeschcke, *Beschreibung . . . Niessen*, Pl. XVIII. For the tall bottle, No. 50, cf. also Froehner, *op. cit.*, Pl. CCXVIII; G. Eisen, *Glass*, Fig. 174.

53. 86.35. This represents one of the most common types of Roman glassmaking popular in the Near East and in Europe. The exterior is often decorated with engraved lines. Cf. A. Kisa, *Das Glas im Altertume*, Formtafel, No. 264; C. Isings, *Roman Glass from Dated Finds*, No. 51b; and recently Joan Liversidge, "Roman Discoveries from Hauxton," *Proc. Ant. Soc.*, LI, 1958, p. 12, No. 2.

54. 86.48. Cf. C. Isings, *Roman Glass from Dated Finds*, No. 36b.

55. 31.411. For color and foot construction cf. the group of jugs mentioned under No. 44 (*Glass from the Ancient World*, No. 274). Head applications on glass vessels are copied from metal prototypes, cf. C. Simonett, *Tessiner Gräberfelder*, Pl. 13, No. 7. Popular in the 2nd and 3rd century, they are usually placed below the handle. A large number of broken-off applications have come down to us while only a few vessels with these attachments are preserved. Cf. J. Liversidge "Roman Discoveries from Hauxton," *Proc. Ant. Soc.*, LI, 1958, pp. 8ff.; G. Sangiorgi, *Vetri antichi*, No. 82; F. Fremersdorf, *Das naturfarbene . . . Glas*, Pls. 12–13; *Glass from the Ancient World*, No. 192; R. Joffroy, "Note sur une oenochoe en verre trouvée à Vertault (Côte d'Or)," *Bull. Soc. Arch. et Hist. du Chatillonnais*, 3, No. 10, 1958, pp. 282–284.

56. 01.7450; purchased from A. Khayat. A type particularly frequent in Syria. Some museums have large quantities; for example, Toledo owns about 50. Cf. *Ancient and*

Near Eastern Glass, The Toledo Museum of Art, n.d., ca. 1961, p. 14; *Glass from the Ancient World*, Nos. 338–39; P. P. Kahane, "Some Aspects of Ancient Glass from Israel," *Antiquity and Survival*, II, Nos. 2–3, 1957, Fig. 37. The most elaborate specimen was formerly J. P. Morgan collection, *Glass from The Corning Museum of Glass*, 1958, No. 19.

57: 18.264; **58:** 93.13; **59:** 30.403. A group of very popular glass types; cf. G. Eisen, *Glass*, pp. 429ff.

60. 01.8227; purchased in Boston by E. Robinson from Azeez Khayat. A type found frequently in the Near East and in western Europe, particularly the Rhineland. It was used as a toilet bottle for bathing. Cf. *Glass from the Ancient World*, No. 203; C. Isings, *Roman Glass from Dated Finds*, No. 61; F. Fremersdorf, *Das naturfarbene . . . Glas*, Pl. 41; M. Vanderhoeven, *Verres romains*, pp. 77ff. For rim construction cf. A. Kisa, *Das Glas im Altertume*, Formtafel, No. 161.

61. 30.394. For its use as a lamp cf. Grace M. Crowfoot and D. B. Harden, "Early Byzantine and Later Glass Lamps," *Journal of Egypt. Arch.*, 17, 1931, pp. 196–208. Cf. also C. Isings, *Roman Glass from Dated Finds*, pp. 126–131; D. B. Harden, *Karanis*, pp. 155ff. For decoration cf. G. Caputo, "Scavi Sahariani," *Monumenti Antichi*, XLI, Rome, 1951, Pl. III, cols. 298ff.; Froehner, *Collection Gréau*, Pl. CXXI.

62. 94.203. Similar to a group of slightly larger vases in Corning (*Glass from the Ancient World*, No. 423), Metropolitan Museum (G. Eisen, *Glass*, Pl. 155), Yale University Art Gallery (*ibid.*), The Hague (*Glass door de eeuwen*, 1957, No. 3), Damascus, Tel Aviv, Rome, Sangiorgi collection (*Vetri antichi*, No. 90), and Berlin (*Journal of Glass Studies*, IV, 1962, p. 65, Fig. 11A). Formerly assigned to late Roman times, they should, in view of vessels with identical decoration such as long necked bottles (G. Eisen, *Glass*, Pl. 155; *Journal of Glass Studies*, *loc. cit.*, pp. 65–66) and perfume vials, be assigned to the early Islamic period.

63. 50.1741. Closely related to a group of so-called Byzantine glasses with cut geometric decoration; many or all in this group may be Sassanian. Cf. two similar vessels in London, Victoria and Albert Museum (D. B. Honey, *Glass*, Pl. 14A) and Rome, Sangiorgi collection (*Vetri antichi*, No. 137). Cf. for the whole problem A. v. Saldern, "Achaemenid and Sassanian Cut Glass," *Ars Orientalis*, 1963, pp. 12ff.; *Jb. d. Hamburger Kunsts.*, 1968. Published: A. v. Saldern, *MFA Bulletin*, 64, 1966, p. 15f., Fig. 14.

64. 29.967. For this frequent type cf. C. J. Lamm, *Mittelalterliche Gläser*, Pls. 20–21. Published: A. v. Saldern, *MFA Bulletin*, 64, 1966, p. 15f., Fig. 15.

65. 31.133. This and the glasses in the following group are representative examples of late Sassanian and Islamic mold-blown ware; recent excavations in Iran and Iraq have added many hitherto unknown patterns to the store of designs published by Lamm in his *Mittelalterliche Gläser*. For a group of similar jugs with Cufic inscriptions cf. D. S. Rice, "Early Signed Islamic Glass," *Journal of the Royal Asiatic Soc.*, April, 1958, pp. 8ff.

66: 18.265; **67:** 30.218; **68:** 30.225. Cf. *Glass from the Ancient World*, Nos. 466ff.

69. 18.273. For Islamic thread decorated glass cf. C. J. Lamm, *Mittelalterliche Gläser*, Pls. 30ff.

70. 30.393. Cf. C. J. Lamm, *Mittelalterliche Gläser*, Pl. 166. Published: A. v. Saldern, *MFA Bulletin*, 64, 1966, p. 16f., Fig. 16.